THE WORLD OF
ANDY CAPP

by
Reg Smythe

MIRROR PUBLICATIONS

INTRODUCTION

Here we are—the festive season.

As usual Andy's told Flo to go out and buy herself a little present—a gold locket, perhaps. Something nice. The trouble is he means exactly what he says—no money changes hands.

Flo's almost finished the Christmas shopping. (Why do women stock up for three weeks when the shops close for less than one?) She's also nearly finished knitting yet another pullover for Andy's present.

The garlands and the silver Christmas tree have been brought down from the loft and dusted off. Flo's hoping Andy will decorate the front room—drawing pins pressed into holes made years ago.

The day itself is likely to be an anti-climax for Andy. He'll try on the pullover. The sleeves will be too long. Then he'll get some useless present from his mum-in-law like a screwdriver or a paintbrush. Silly old . . . !

Flo will open his present to her and try to look surprised. She'll spend half the day cooking poultry (or should I say overcooking it) when he would much rather have steak and kidney pie.

He'll sleep through an old film, a circus, a chat show and a so-called comedy . . . he'll wake up . . . he'll feel let down. Then he'll remember why.

The one night of the year when we're all *supposed* to be celebrating is the one night of the year when Jackie doesn't open the pub!

It doesn't make sense.

Cheers,

Reg. Smythe

ANDY CAPP

ORIGINAL CARTOON OFFER

A framed, original Andy Capp cartoon can be yours!

'OI, FANCY OWNIN' A FRAMED PICTURE OF ME?

Due to the enormous popularity of Andy Capp, we have decided to offer a selection of original cartoons by Reg Smythe for just £55.00 each! Available at this price through this offer only. Just fill in the form below and post off your order today! We regret that it is impossible to supply specific cartoons of your choice.

S174

THE MOST REMARKABLE THING ABOUT THAT BLOKE'S STORIES IS HOW HE MANAGES TO GET HOME TO *TELL* THEM

I SOMETIMES WONDER HOW YOU *REALLY* FEEL ABOUT ME, PET—

WOULD YOU SWOP ME?

NEVER

S175

HE'S JUST AS GOOD AS ANY OTHER BLOKE—

EXCEPT THAT HE HAS A SMALLER PERCENTAGE OF ACTIVE INGREDIENTS

C'MON, NOW, GET Y'SELF UP

— THE BOOKIE AND THE BREWERY'LL BE SENDING OUT A SEARCH PARTY!

ENJOYED THAT, DID YOU?!

HEH! HEH! HEH! HEH! HEH! HEH! HEH—!

SORRY I'M A BIT LATE, PET. THEY ASKED ME TO WORK AN HOUR'S OVERTIME—

YOU'RE NOT GOING OUT NOW, ARE YOU?!

LOOK, I'VE BEEN IN ALL AFTERNOON—YOU CAN'T EXPECT ME TO STAY HOME HALF THE EVENING AS WELL

SELFISH —THAT'S ME

S248

YOU WERE AT THAT BAR FOR NEARLY AN HOUR TALKING T' THAT WOMAN —AN' THERE'S ME STUCK HERE LIKE A LEMON

I FELT SORRY FOR HER, FLO — SHE'S ALL ON HER OWN

I RECKON THE QUICKEST WAY FOR ME TO GET OVER THIS CHILL IS TO SPEND THE DAY IN BED ....

S249

THAT'S IF YOU DON'T MIND GETTING THE MEALS READY...

NOT AT ALL, PET, NOT AT ALL. MY PLEASURE

BE A LOVELY CHANGE TO HAVE HER GRIPE ABOUT MY COOKING INSTEAD OF MY IDLENESS

S294

S295

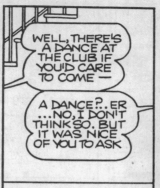

© 1985 Mirror Publications Ltd.
First published in Great Britain in October 1985 by Mirror Publications Ltd., Maxwell House, 74 Worship Street,
London EC2A 2EN for Mirror Group Newspapers Ltd.
Colour printing by The Friary Press, Dorchester. Printed in Great Britain by Spottiswoode Ballantyne Printers Ltd., Colchester and London.
Distributed by Argus Press Sales & Distribution Ltd., London.
0 85939 409 5